THE ROOTS OF EVIL

John Howard visiting a Prison F. *Wheatley del.*

Frontispiece]